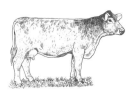

BEAUTIFUL COWS

JOURNAL

Ivy Press

A COW SPOTTER'S FIELD GUIDE

GLOUCESTER

Where seen..

Date..

Notes..

LONGHORN

Where seen..

Date..

Notes..

ANKOLE WATUSI

Where seen..

Date..

Notes..

BRAUNVIEH

Where seen..

Date..

Notes..

TEXAS LONGHORN

Where seen..

Date..

Notes..

AYRSHIRE

Where seen..

Date..

Notes..

CHAROLAIS

Where seen..

Date..

Notes..

BRAVADO

Where seen..

Date..

Notes..

LONGHORN
4-YEAR-OLD COW

Not to be confused with the Texas Longhorn, the LONGHORN is solidly English and was Britain's first true cattle breed. It was developed by eighteenth-century breeder Robert Bakewell of Leicestershire specifically for the butcher. His most famous bull was Twopenny. Twopenny's more valuable grandson was named 'D' (which stood for penny).

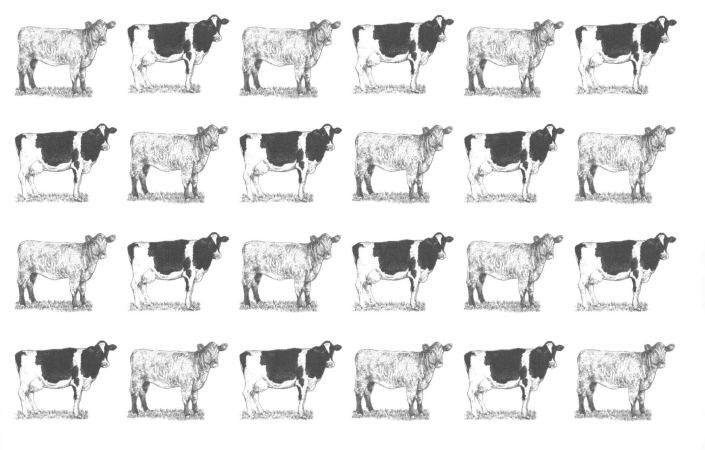

ANKOLE WATUSI
8-YEAR-OLD COW

Many native African cows have been selectively bred for centuries, primarily for looks such as striking coat patterns and colours. The Ankole cattle of East Africa have been bred for impressive horns and for their milk. The most dramatic of all Ankole cattle are the ANKOLE WATUSI of the Tutsi tribes, now seen in Europe and the USA.

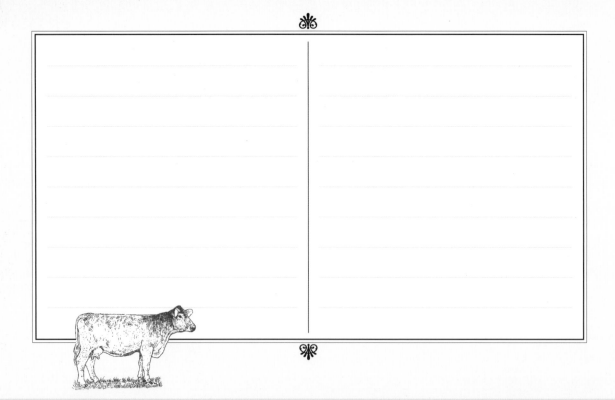

BRAUNVIEH
4-YEAR-OLD COW

Mentioned in Swiss medieval records, BRAUNVIEH grazed Alpine pastures. European and North American interest led nineteenth-century Swiss breeders to take them more seriously, specifying that they should be brown, and supply ample milk and meat. Braunviehs were developed into the American Brown Swiss dairy cow in the USA.

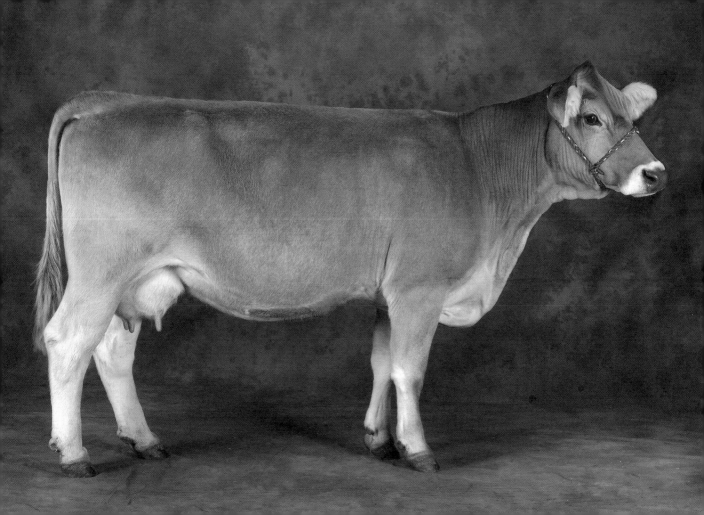

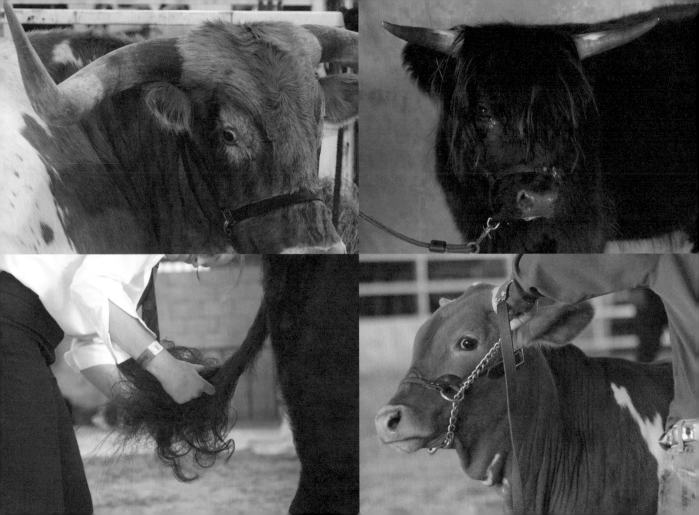

TEXAS LONGHORN
4-YEAR-OLD COW

Think cowboy, and you think TEXAS LONGHORN: they are forever associated with the romance of the Wild West but their history dates back to Spanish cattle brought over to Santo Domingo in the 1490s and later into Mexico. In about 1690, herds of these cattle were driven from Mexico to the Sabine River and what would become Texas.

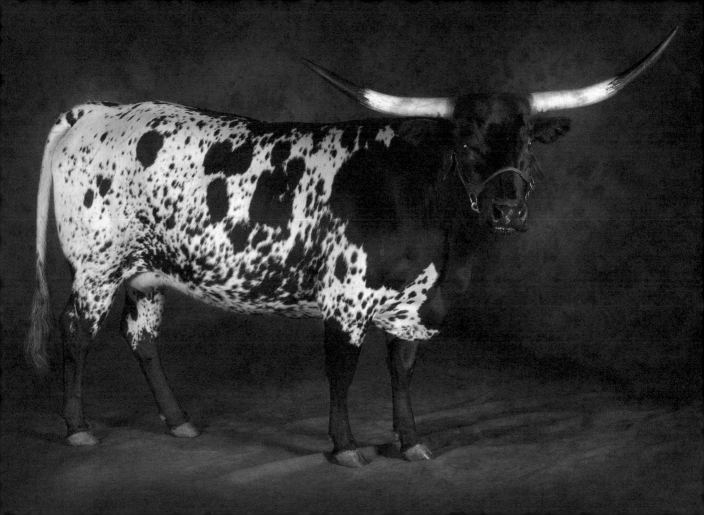

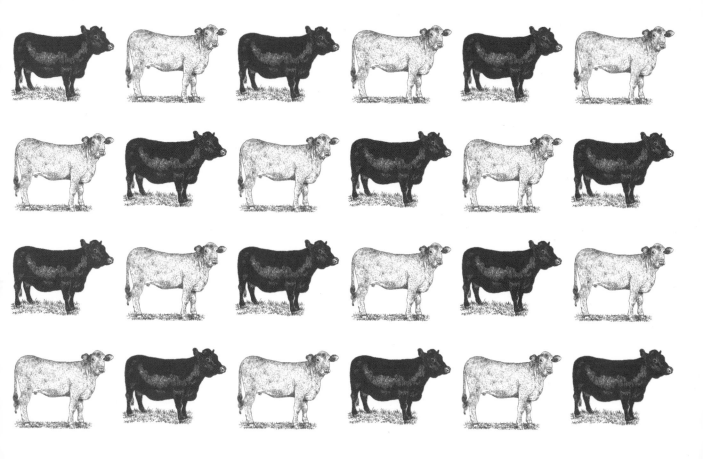

AYRSHIRE
8-YEAR-OLD COW

Scotland's only native dairy breed, graceful AYRSHIRE cows were the darlings of the show-ring in the nineteenth century. In 1929, two Ayrshire cows were walked from Brandon, Vermont, to the National Dairy Show at St. Louis, Missouri, as a publicity stunt. Both cows went on to beat milk-yield records of their time.

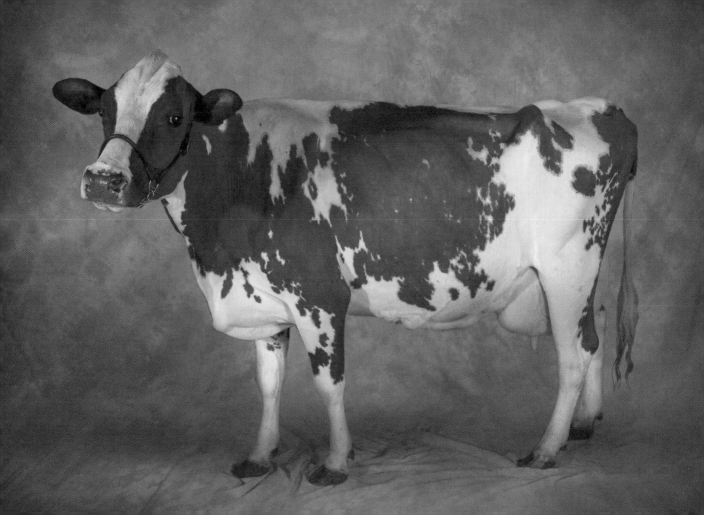

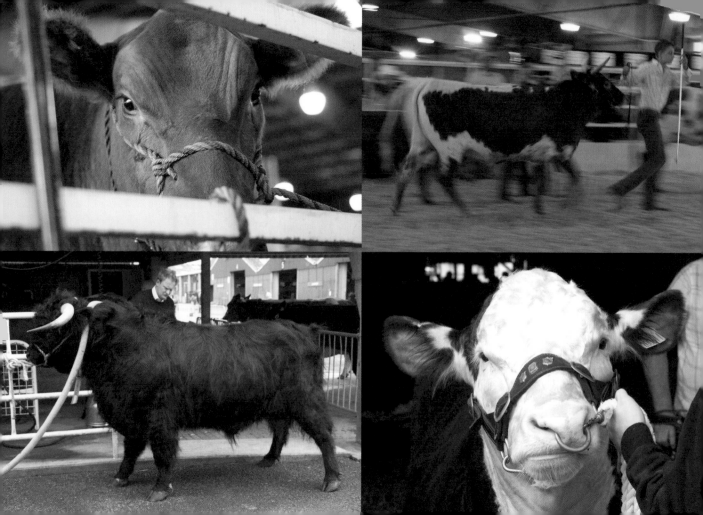

CHAROLAIS
2-YEAR-OLD COW

France's CHAROLAIS led the Continental charge into the world's beef herds in the late 1950s. Selectively bred by farmers around Charolle in the eighteenth century, these hefty cattle crossed the Atlantic in 1930, imported into Mexico by Jean Pugibet. The celebrated King Ranch and other Texan ranches imported some of his bulls in 1936.

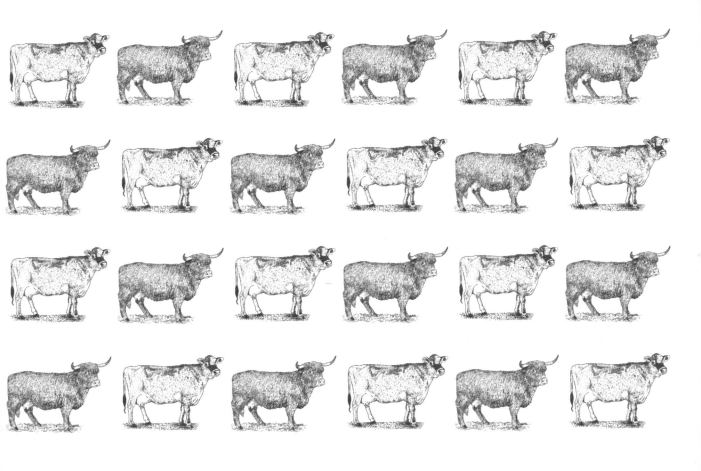

BRAVADO
2-YEAR-OLD HEIFER

Like the Brahmousin, this breed combines the French Limousin with the humped Brahman. In 1986 at the Rottmann Ranch, Oklahoma, a Polled Limousin cow was mated with a Red Brahman bull, and their calf, Diablo, became the father of the BRAVADO breed. All full-blood Bravados trace back to the ranch's original Polled Limousin stock.

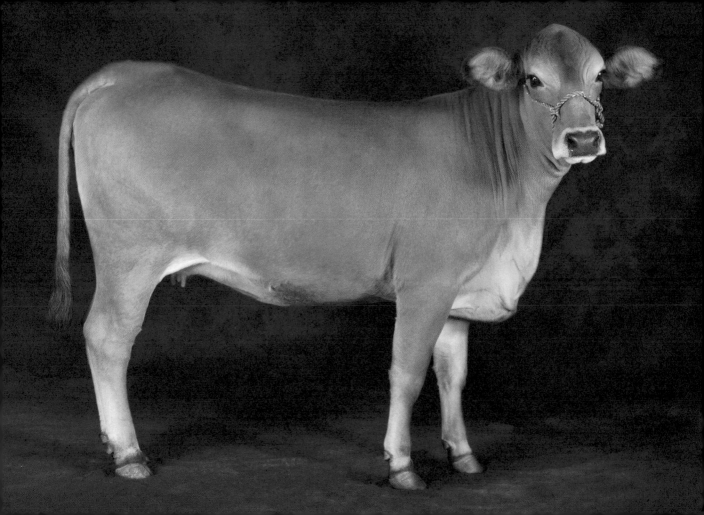

BRITISH WHITE
7-YEAR-OLD COW

A tangled tale of abbeys, parks and stately halls created the BRITISH WHITE, which had its eighteenth-century roots at Whalley Abbey and Gunton Park; then, in the nineteenth century, Blickling and Woodbastwick. Classified as a rare breed in the 1970s, its growing popularity has upgraded it to a minority breed.

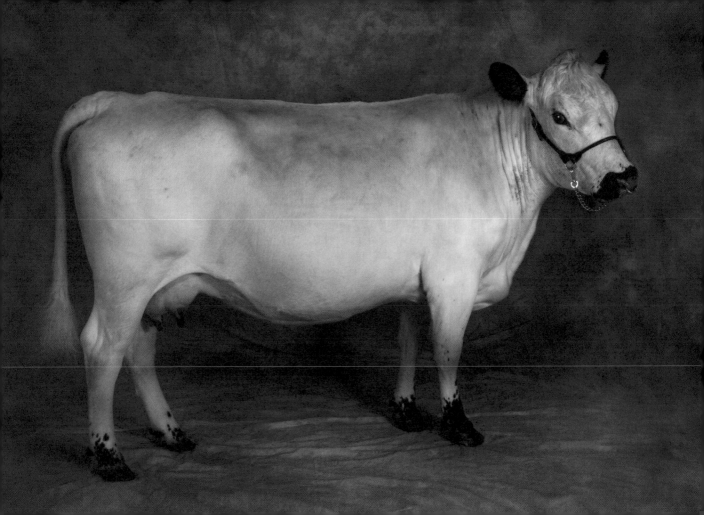

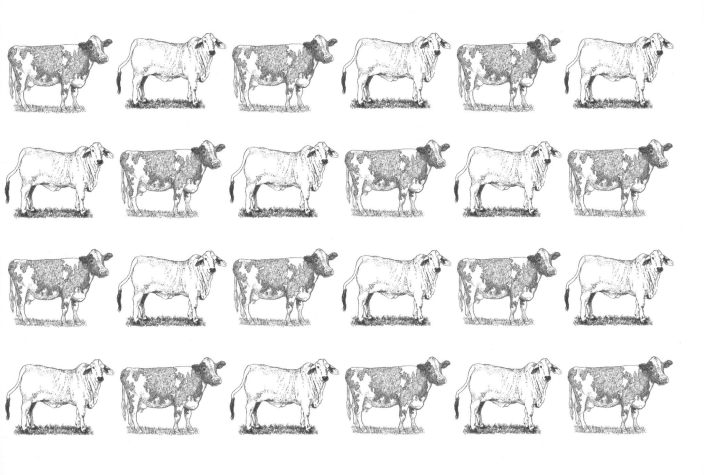

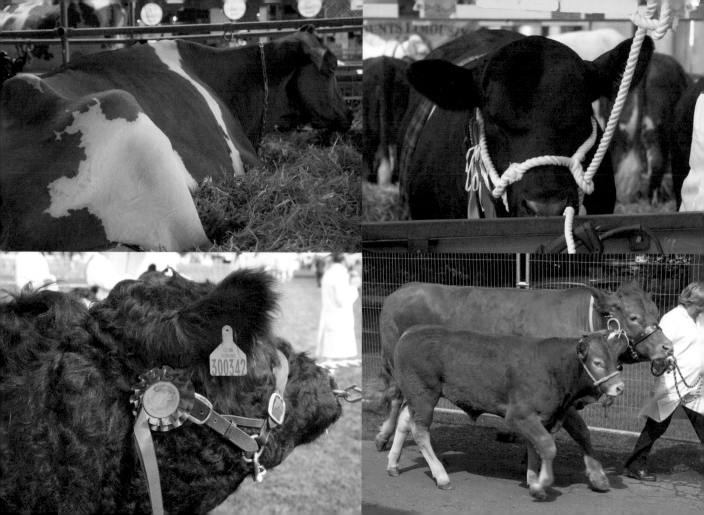

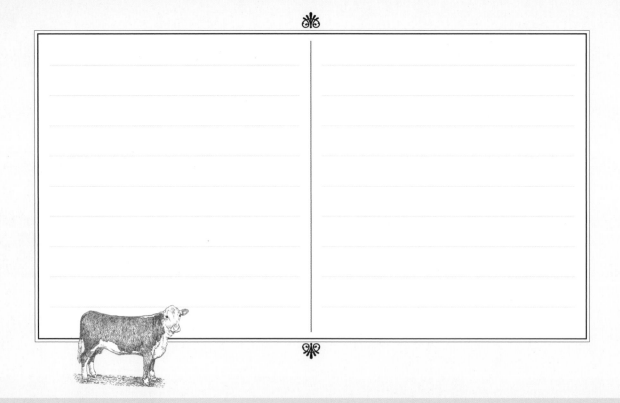

HEREFORD
3-YEAR-OLD COW

This Welsh Marches breed stamped its famous face on beef herds from the ranches of the American West and South American pampas to the plains of Africa in the nineteenth century. Herefords were considered 'pleasant, cheerful, open' in the 1850s, but the progeny of a Hereford bull crossed with a Kyloe cow were 'extremely pugnacious'.

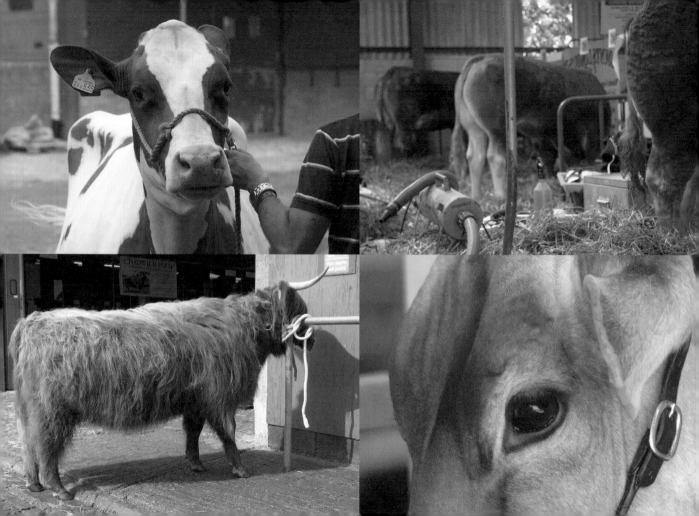

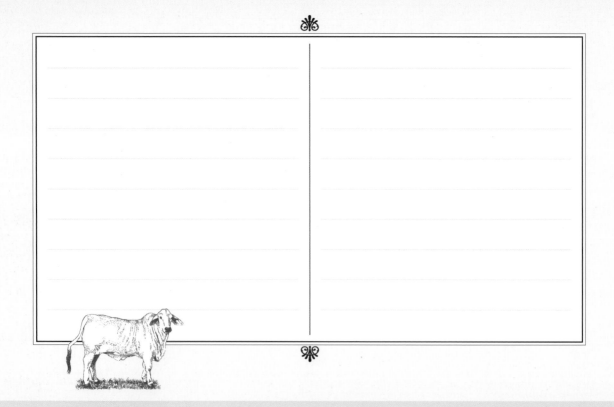

BRAHMAN
2-YEAR-OLD COW

The BRAHMAN is a successful fusion of the East and West. In 1849, the first zebus were imported into the USA. Years later, the British government gave two Indian zebu bulls to a plantation owner for teaching the British how to grow cotton and sugar. Gradually other zebus arrived and from them the Brahman grew.

SIMMENTAL
3-YEAR-OLD COW

Switzerland is the home of this gentle, motherly but rugged cow: the all-purpose Simmentals which originated in the Simme Valley. A Simmental cow born in Switzerland in 1915 produced at the age of 14 a phenomenal 11,902 kg (26,240 lb) of milk in what was to be her last lactation – she kept on pouring it out for 498 days.

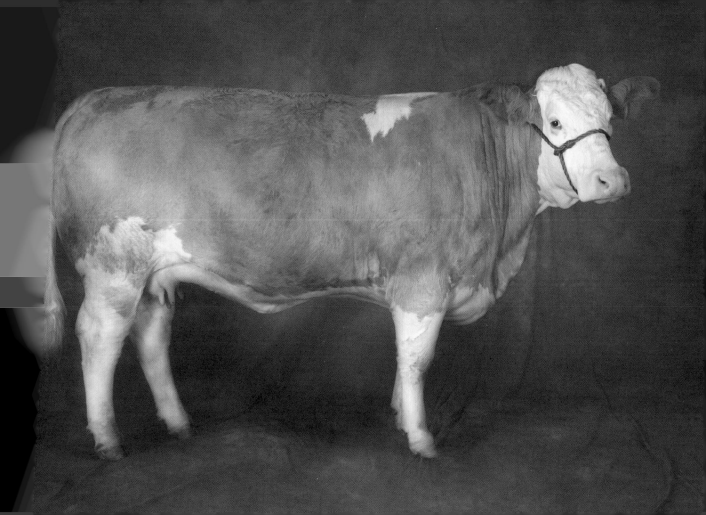

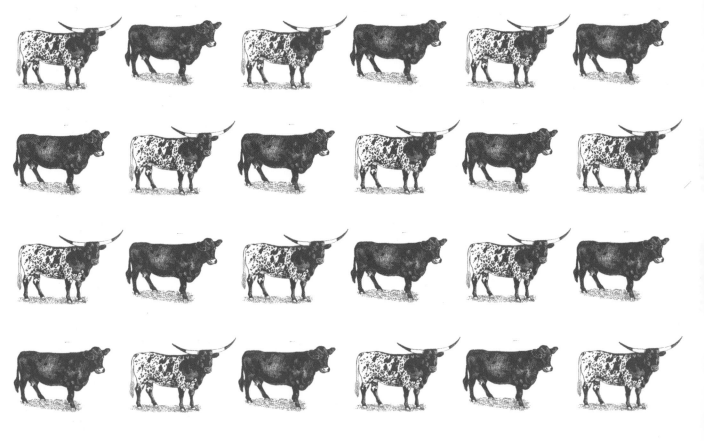

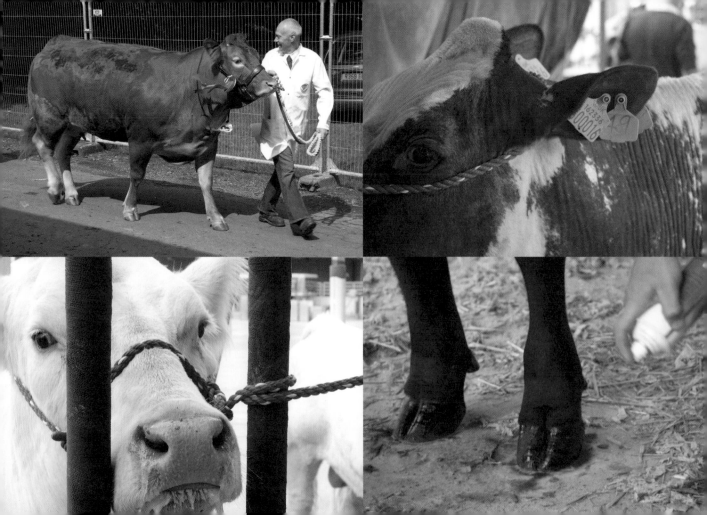

HOLSTEIN
6-YEAR-OLD COW

There has been much name-swapping of this breed between HOLSTEIN and Friesian. 'Holstein' was first used when cows from Schleswig-Holstein followed settlers to nineteenth-century America. Since then they have crept back to Europe: Friesians made up 86 per cent of the British dairy herd in 1982 but by 2000, Holsteins had taken over.

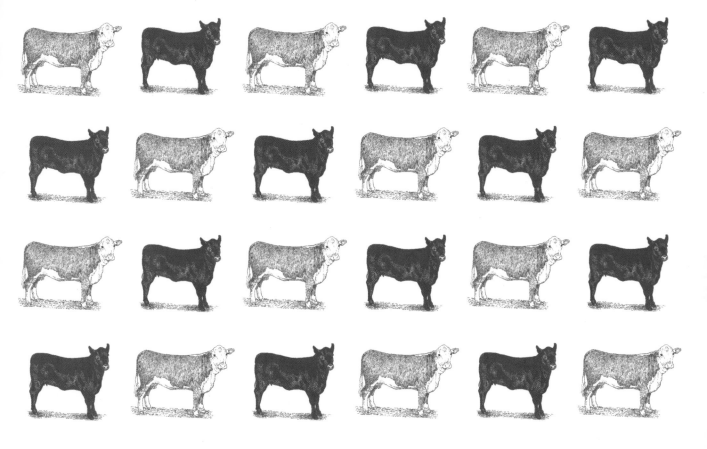

the like cour

JERSEY
2-YEAR-OLD COW

The island of Jersey is renowned for its distinctive cows: there are, for example, 600,000 Jersey cows in New Zealand and 400,000 in the USA. There is a theory that, since fishermen from Jersey were fishing off Newfoundland in the fifteenth century, perhaps Jersey cows landed in Canada much earlier than officially recorded.

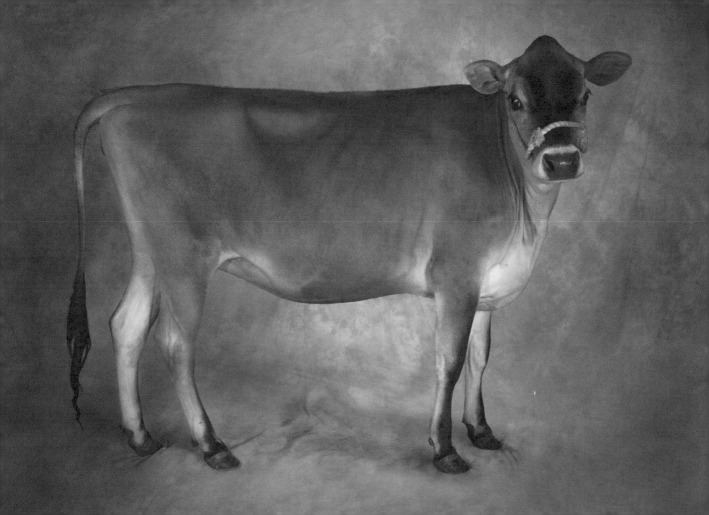

HIGHLAND
4-YEAR-OLD HEIFER

Scotland's HIGHLAND cattle are tough enough to withstand rigorous conditions and so hairy that they could be mistaken for horned yaks. One of Britain's purest breeds, they have been improved by selection rather than cross-breeding. Prior to the twentieth century, they used to be swum across the straits between islands and the mainland.

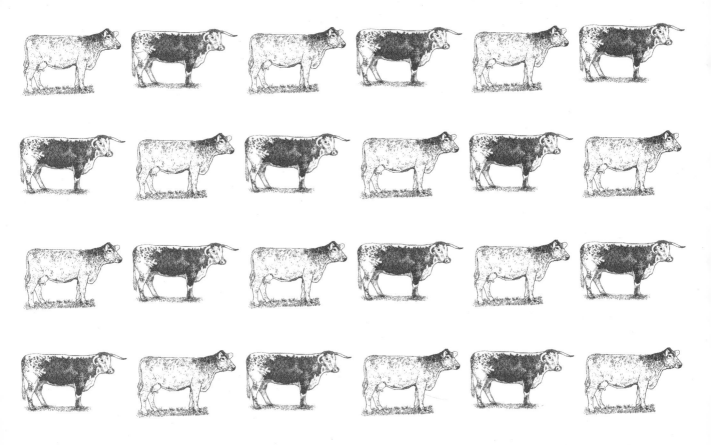

BRAHMOUSIN
1-YEAR-OLD HEIFER

The BRAHMOUSIN is a combination of the subtropical Brahman with the temperate Limousin. In the 1970s, Daryl Wiggins, of Texas, received embryos from a Limousin cow called Gloria. He began a cross-breeding programme with Brahman cattle which led to a mixture that was ultimately five-eighths Limousin and three-eighths Brahman.

First published in the UK in 2010 by
Ivy Press
210 High Street
Lewes
East Sussex BN7 2NS
United Kingdom
www.ivypress.co.uk

ISBN: 978-1-907332-13-5

British Library Cataloguing-in-Publication Data
A catalogue record for this book is available from
the British Library

This book was conceived, designed and produced by
Ivy Press

Printed in China

10 9 8 7 6 5 4 3 2 1